Did You Know?

Alexia Tatianna

Did You Know?

ISBN: 978-0-578-71483-7

I give all the glory to Almighty God.
For my son Amir Lee and Emmanuel.

DID YOU KNOW THAT YOUR SMILE LIGHTS UP THE ROOM ?

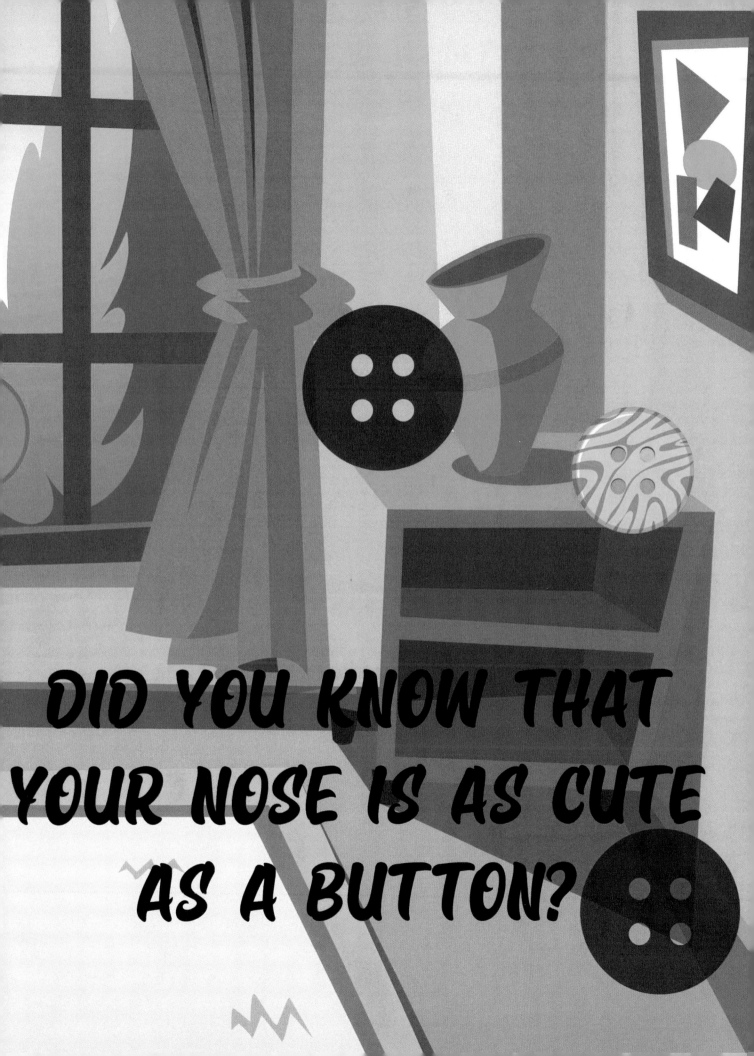

DID YOU KNOW THAT YOUR HAIR IS SOFT LIKE A KITTEN'S FUR?

DID YOU KNOW THAT YOUR SKIN IS MORE PRECIOUS THAN GOLD?

DID YOU KNOW THAT YOU ARE SMART?

DID YOU KNOW THAT YOU ARE STRONG?

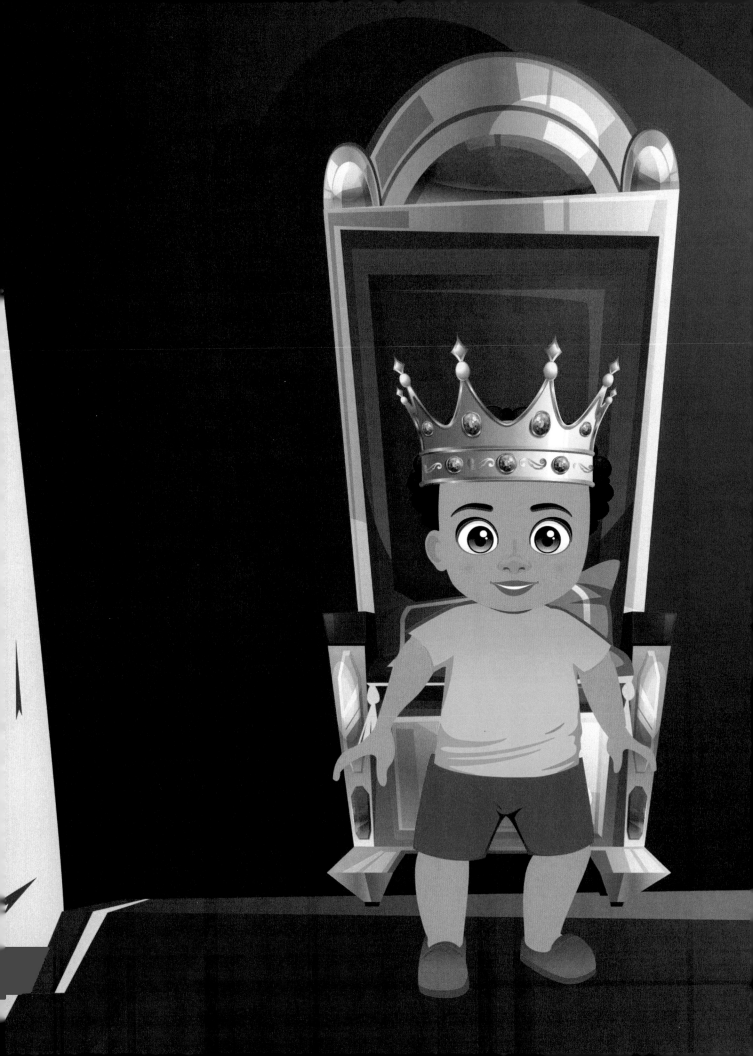

DID YOU KNOW THAT YOU ARE A KING?

DID YOU KNOW THAT YOU ARE LOVED?

The End!

Made in the USA
Monee, IL
08 December 2023

47626799R00017